Oscar
the dog
and friends

by John Cotton

Illustrated by Adrienne Geoghegan

Oscar the Dog

"I'm a barking boy,
Don't deny my name."

I'm Oscar the Dog
I'm my own dog not theirs -
In spite of whatever they think.
So I'll fight and I'll run
And have lots of fun,
And find dirty puddles to drink.

I'm Oscar the Dog
And my breed's Dartmoor Terrier,
And let me tell you for free,
That I bark and I pull,
And I'm never the merrier
Than sniffing and being just me.

I'm Oscar the Dog
And when I am called
I keep them all waiting a while.
Though I go in the end
I like to pretend
I'll run off, 'cause that is my style.

I'm Oscar the Dog
And I'm all for Dogs' Lib,
Though my mistress tells people I'm good,
So I growl at her friends
And water her plants
To make sure it's quite understood,

That I'm Oscar the Dog
And when I'm called bad
I smile and I wag my small tail,
And as for a smack,
It's like a pat on the back,
I tell you it really can't fail!

I'm Oscar the Dog
And I'm everyone's friend
When there's something to offer or give,
A biscuit or tit bit,
I really don't mind,
After all a dog's got to live.

Oscar the Dog says

Sometimes it is difficult to remember I'm not human ...
Toby comes in from work.
"Mmmmm!" he says. "That smells good. What's cooking?"
"Hearts," Mum says.
"Gosh! My favourites. I love hearts."
"They are not for you. They're for Oscar," Mum says.
"Sometimes I think Oscar eats better than I do," says Toby.
"Why don't you give him proper dog food,
Like Pal or Pedigree Chum?"
"I'm not giving Oscar that," says Mum.
"That's for animals."

Oscar the Dog says

I have problems with security ...

Mum has barricaded and boarded
Every opening, gap, space or hole in the
   garden fence.
She's made Stalag 37 out of the place!
Why the bother? When I get out
I only hold up the traffic, dig in gardens,
Or frighten the life out of neighbouring cats.
I'll tell you a secret-
I've been watching 'Colditz' on TV,
When she thinks I'm dozing by the fire,
I'm working on a glider at the back of the garden shed.

Bridgette the Boat Dog

I'm Bridgette the Boat Dog,
I live on a barge,
So while it's not "anchors aweigh",
It is still "let go aft",
And starboard and port,
And locks to manoeuvre each day.

Canal life is busy I'll tell you.
There's polishing and
    keeping things bright.
There's cooking and sewing,
Engines to keep going,
And then I'm the guard dog
    at night!

From Uxbridge to Tring
We sail the Grand Union
And call in at pubs on our way.
At the 'Three Horseshoes' or 'Boat',
At the 'Sunrise' or 'Goat'
We take our refreshments each day.

There are plenty of friends on the Boatways,
Other barges, with their dogs as well.
Then there are mallards and coots,
And fierce honking geese
Who give us a sailors' farewell!

So it's quite a good life as a Boat Dog
When the mornings are fresh and
     sun-bright,
And the evening is peaceful and settling
As the sun sets and softens the light.

Roger the old dog

Roger is an old dog,
He likes to sleep as much as he can
And dream his dreams like any old man.
His hide is scuffed and scarred and tough
For Roger when young had lived it rough.

He likes to roast himself by the fire.
He likes it the better when the flames
   lick higher
Up the chimney, and if a spark should fall
And burn his rough old coat at all,
He might roll over to put it out,
But he won't be hurried,
And Roger is certainly not at all worried.

"There are worse things in Rome," Roger
   will say.
But if you ask him what, he will look away
And attend to some scratching or the licking
   of paws.
He's not answering silly questions like yours!

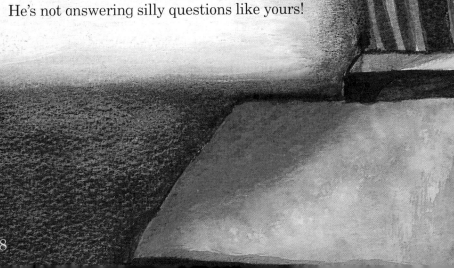

Olive Barker

Olive Barker is a shaggy dog,
Lively and full of noise,
She barks about and barks about
Not caring if it annoys!

She will bark when there's danger
She will bark when there's not,
The fact is Olive just barks a lot!

If Olive is out walking
She will suddenly stop,
Up goes her head
And out will pop
Yap, bark, yap, bark,
Yap, bark, yap, bark,
All over the park!

She will go out in the
    evening
Under a star bright sky,
Then she will start,
We don't know why,
Yap, bark, yap, bark,
Yap, bark, yap, bark,
Shattering the dark!

Dad says she'll have to go,
And Mum looks sad,
But there is no doubt
That Olive's barking is bad
And already driven
Several neighbours mad!

A postman or the milkman
Only have to come near
And Olive is off again I fear,
And it's
Yap, bark, yap, bark,
Yap, bark, yap, bark,
For all to hear!

So what can we do?
She surely mustn't go!
"Can't help it," she says,
"It's my nature you know."
And then looks so pleading
With her big sad eyes.
"We'll just have to put up with it,"
Mother sighs.

Oscar the Dog says

It's a wonder I don't have an identity problem ...

I get called "Good Boy", "Little Man",
And even "Old Fellow".
"Keep your muddy feet off the carpet,"
Mum (she calls herself my Mum!) says.
Haven't they noticed I've a leg at each corner
With paws at the end of them?
And I'm covered in fur!
A bit of dogism wouldn't be amiss.

Oscar the Dog says

I have a problem communicating with the natives ...

A growl or a tail-wag works all right for basic needs;

But for anything complicated, subtle,
Or verging on the sophisticated
They're as thick as bloodhounds!
I've even tried barking in French:
Je voudrais ...
But to no avail.
I'll just have to remember in future
To bark slowly and loudly.

Sally the Yorkie

I'm Sally the Yorkie
And although I'm quite small
I'll not take saucy
Comments at all.

I know my coat's silky
Which causes remarks
When my mistress takes me
For walks in the parks.

But I don't care how big
Another dog may be,
I'll not let anyone
Be cheeky to me.

So if any dog growls
In an unpleasant way
Or shows me his teeth
Then I'll start an affray!

And let it be known
I do not know fear,
And there's many a
    mastiff
With my mark on his ear!

Sexton the Bloodhound

He's hunted down robbers in Dawlish,
In Brighton crooks fear him you know,
While he was down in St Ives
He sussed out some dives,
And he's closed up some dens in Soho.

In Banbury he arrested a bandit,
And in Stepney he stamped out a gang,
While he detected the five desperados
Who cunningly stole from Barnados
A consignment of lemon meringue!

In Kettering he cornered kidnappers,
In Derby prevented a fraud,
And for daring and courage when dealing with spies
Who had sent secret messages hidden in pies,
He was given a bravery award.

People remember his exploits in Ealing,
His skill in catching Blue Cloud,
And they still talk in Crewe
Of when he arrested Sharp Sue
And her sidekick the Mob Leader Maud.

THE DERBY ECHO

SEXTON SNIFFS OUT SWINDLERS

BLOODHOUND FINDS BANBURY BANDITS

BANBURY POST

KETTERING COMET

SEXTON CORNERS KETTERING KIDNAPPERS

SOHO STAR

SEXTON CLOSES DENS

For Sexton's an ace detective
Who leads the Canine Squad,
Why even the Police Commissioner
Gives Sexton a friendly nod.
For he can sniff out clues like an expert,
As for tracking he knows his stuff,
All the crooks cry, "Oh! Not Sexton again!
We've really had enough!"

17

Cathy the Collie

I'm a working dog,
Not a shirking dog,
And at the break of day
I'm out on the hillside
Making my way
To find the sheep
Which I herd
And keep in order.

With the help of
   the Shepherd
And his whistles and shouts
I round up the ewes
And those dreadful louts,
The rams so proud
Of their curly horns,
Though they're worse than useless
When they're caught in the thorns!

Then I have to find them
And raise the alarm
So they can get safely
Back to the farm.
Though the busiest time
Is when the lambs are born
Or Spring time when
The sheep are shorn.

So I'm a working dog
Making my way
To my flock on the hills
At the break of day.

In the night

Listening to the silence
In the middle of the night
When a wind-rattling window can give you a fright.
A tap drip, drip, dripping,
A creak on the stair,
Makes you wonder if anyone is there.
No need to worry-
It's the house growing old
And grumbling as it feels the cold
Of the evening when the sun goes down.

Besides, Oscar the Dog is in the hall,
He'll bark off any unwanted call.
His ear is alert, even when he's dozing,
He's ready to leap up at any nosing
Stranger in the house who shouldn't be there
As Oscar keeps guard under the stair.

Alfred the Shepherd

Alfred the Shepherd is a guard dog by night
He patrols the dark corners of a new building site.
He keeps off intruders or maybe a thief
With fierce growly noises and a showing of teeth.

He gives those who approach a crocodile grin
Which acts as a warning not to go in.
But those who are foolish enough to try
Will feel the heat of his breath by and by!

Yet when after work he lies by the fire
He's as gentle as butter and likes to retire
Into himself and dream lovely dreams
Of meadows and mountains and soft running streams.

An Indian Dog

The Taj Mahal in full moonlight,
The mass of marble gently glows
And seems to float in the mystic air.

Across the river, at the back,
A lone dog barks,
And its bark is echoed.
He barks back,
And the echo replies.
And so it goes on
In what could be
A sort of barking infinity!

As the great white tomb
Responds to the moon.

Goodbye

Old Oscar boy is far and gone,
We'll hear his bark no more,
Though his collar and his lead
   still hang
Behind the hallway door.

He's deep in sleep and dreaming
The deepest dream of all,
Of the longest walk he'll ever take
Beyond the garden wall.

And there he's salmon-leaping
In the tall Elysian grass.
Though still at times, I wake
   to think
I've seen his shadow pass.

We wish you well and thank you
For your friendship and your games,
Our love goes with you Oscar
For your memory remains.

But Oscar boy is far and gone,
We'll hear his bark no more,
Though his collar and his lead
   still hang
Behind the hallway door.